D1254645

Created, published, and distributed by Knock Knock
1635-B Electric Ave.
Venice, CA 90291
knockknockstuff.com

Made in China

ISBN: 978-160106822-4
UPC: 825703-50096-7
10 9 8 7 6 5 4 3 2 1

Ussies

A PHOTO ALBUM OF WE, OURSELVES, AND US

A (Very) Brief History of the Ussie

1495-1498

In *The Last Supper*, Leonardo da Vinci paints his subjects—Jesus and his twelve apostles—on one side of a table in order to capture the faces of the entire group.

1930

Grant Wood's well-known *American Gothic* features a portrait of a glum farm couple staring back at the viewer.

1983

Nancy Reagan and Mr. T team up to reveal White House holiday decorations, allowing official photographers to snap one of the first odd-couple ussies.

2012

Meryl Streep and Hillary Clinton are photographed taking an ussie at The Kennedy Center Honors.

2013

A group of Italian teens at St. Peter's Basilica snaps what may be the "first papal selfie" —actually an ussie— with Pope Francis.

2013

President Obama and the prime ministers of Denmark and Great Britain take a group shot at Nelson Mandela's memorial service, raising eyebrows around the world.

1985

Michael Jackson, Bruce Springsteen, Stevie Wonder and a cast of musicians take an all-star ussie during the recording of "We Are the World."

1992

The first picture ever uploaded to the web is a group shot of an all-girl band made up of scientists' girlfriends at CERN, the European particle physics research lab.

2008

Snoop Dogg appears on Martha Stewart's cooking show, resulting in a publicity photo he will post on his Instagram account six years later as a #tbt.

2014

The Dalai Lama joins Instagram and begins to post pictures with friends including Larry King, a sumo wrestler, and university students.

2014

Ellen DeGeneres' celebrity-packed Oscars ussie with Bradley Cooper and Julia Roberts (among others) becomes the most retweeted tweet of all time.

2016

Knock Knock introduces Ussies: A Photo Album of We, Ourselves, and Us.

5 Simple Tips for Taking Your Ussie

1. LIKE A BOSS

Take charge of your ussie. Ask the person with the longest arms to snap the picture. For large groups, people in the back should stand and people in the front should be seated. Tell everyone to make sure they can be seen in the shot and count it down so everyone is ready. For really large groups, consider the selfie stick—perhaps a bit conspicuous, but it really does allow you to fit in more people. And remember to take multiple shots!

2. KNOW YOUR ANGLES

Put your smartphone in landscape mode—the horizontal format is better for a group. As an accomplished photographer of the selfie, you should already know your own best side, so make sure you get it. And remember—the most flattering pics are usually those shot from above the subjects.

3. SET DESIGN 101

Make sure your background isn't cluttered or crowded (unless that's the effect you want). Avoid positioning people's heads so that they are bisected by the horizon line. And take one last quick glance behind you before you snap to avoid the photobomb.

4. GO TOWARD THE LIGHT

Any photographer will tell you it's all about the light. Whether that means going outside, facing a window, or just turning on a few lamps, know that a filter can only do so much.

5. TELL EVERYONE TO SMILE!

Or not.

When the ruins of our modern society are discovered at some point in the distant future, chances are high that archeologists will determine an irrefutable truth about us: we had absolutely no issues with putting ourselves out there.

We are a nation of oversharers—informing friends, family, and sometimes strangers what we're all wearing, eating, thinking, and doing at any and every given moment.

So in addition to snapping photos of our food, our pets, and the random sunset with our camera-enabled smartphones, it only makes sense that we document ourselves with our friends, family, and sweethearts.

Why? Is it because, freed from the time and expense of developing film, we're all budding photographers? Or is it just that we really, really, really like to show we're part of a couple or a tribe? Maybe it's simply a way to remember that special day, that wild party, or that romantic moment. Whatever the reason, this photo album is a way to collect and keep those group portraits worth saving.

Us

Us

Us

Us again

Us

On vacay

Us

#soblessed

Us

Us, us, us

Us

Party ussie!

Us

NSFW

Us

This. Always.

Us

Romantic us

Us

Photobombed!

Us

Yeah, we're weirdos

Us

Too cute

Us

Look at us!

Us

YOLO

Us

Stuffing our faces

Us

So. Totally. Us.

Us

Goofing off

Us

We ♥ this

Us

Us being us

Us

#tbt

Us

Celebrating

Us

SMOOCH!

Us

#us, # ____________________

Us

Oh hello, there!

Happy!!!

Us

Having some "we" time

Us

You. Me. Us.